Contents

Teachers' notes

The aim of the activities in this book is to support the implementation of the National Curriculum for geography, with particular reference to physical geography and geographical skills. The activities should not be seen as teaching tools in themselves, but as opportunities for children to develop newly-acquired knowledge and skills. This particularly applies to activities 10 and 11: UK weather forecast; 16: Relief rainfall; 17: Convectional rainfall; 26 and 27: Hurricane!, and 32: World climates. These activities will require some pre-teaching before being used with the children, though they can also be used as an important part of that teaching process. It would be very useful to have examples of weather maps from a range of newspapers, as well as copies of weather maps from local centres or even from the UK Weather Centre at Bracknell in Berkshire. Another useful aid would be satellite photographs of UK weather as well as video recordings of different weather forecasts for the same days over a period of a week. This will allow pupils to compare style of map symbols, accuracy and general approach to weather forecasting.

The aims of this book

The aims of this book are:
• to introduce children to the different elements of weather, from temperature to wind (speed and direction), precipitation (rain, snow, hail) and cloud cover;
• to introduce children to the idea of climate as 'average' weather;
• to develop the idea that weather has an important impact on a wide range of human activities from walking, farming and playing to going on holiday;
• to show that different parts of the world have different weather and climate; and
• to show how children can investigate and record microclimates such as around the school.

Geographical content

Weather is one of the most fundamental topics studied by children in primary schools. It has a profound influence on many aspects of their lives, from the clothes they wear to the games they play and even to their mental attitude. Studies of weather provide an excellent opportunity to combine geographical work with scientific work. Teachers have long developed lessons which deal with the measurement and recording of the many aspects of weather such as temperature, wind, cloud and precipitation and so on. The geographical dimensions to this work at Key Stage 2 are:
• an emphasis on the impact of different weather on people's daily lives (pages 5, 6, 7, 18, 19, 20, 22, 23, 25);
• the investigation of microclimate (pages 8, 9);
• maps of weather forecasts for the UK and Europe (pages 10, 11, 12, 13, 14, 15);
• the causes of different types of rainfall (pages 16 and 17);
• the impact of dramatic weather (pages 24, 26, 27);
• the distinction between weather and climate (pages 5 and 28);
• the description of different types of climate in different parts of the world (pages 28, 29, 30, 31, 32).

The aim of these activities is to provide opportunities to widen the geographical experiences of children working at Key Stage 2. They are designed to be both fun and interesting and also often involve an element of human drama, such as Hurricane! (26, 27) and Rescue! (24). There is scope within projects on weather for children to step beyond mere observation and recording of weather, and to use their imagination to investigate dramatic events such as snowstorms.

It is also important for children to become familiar with the range of different maps and satellite images used in weather forecasting. As the process of weather forecasting becomes increasingly hi-tech the use and availability of satellite images of the UK to show features such as cloud position has become common, on television and in newspaper forecasts. Teachers need to ensure that children see what they see in the satellite images, for example, pick out the shape of the UK and identify places with cloud and places with sunshine. Similarly, the use of computer-generated symbols is also common to show how weather patterns are expected to develop over the coming days. Children may need help in distinguishing computer-generated images from satellite images and from general synoptic weather charts.

Children's main interest is bound to lie in the variations in local weather. However, their interest in weather conditions elsewhere in the world should be encouraged. Sometimes an event such as flood or hurricane will focus media attention on another part of the world and so provide an opportunity for extending the scope of the children's study. In other cases television programmes (including soaps) may well provide an introduction to weather characteristics in other places.

Notes on individual activities

Page 5: What is the weather?

The purpose of this activity is to highlight the key elements which make up weather – temperature, precipitation (rain, snow, hail), wind and sunshine. A second purpose is to emphasise that weather is the day to day changes in the local atmosphere, whilst climate (see page 28) is the average of these changes over several years. Climate is really the average weather of an area over a substantial period. Ask the children to identify as many different ways in which weather affects human activities. The teacher may want to classify these into weather conditions which help people (sunshine to ripen crops or for holidays) or which threaten people (snowstorms, fog).
Extension: Ask the children to draw pictures which show different weather at different times of the year,

such as winter snow, autumn fog and frost, summer wind and spring sunshine, and highlight their effects on human activities.

Pages 6 and 7: Weather and clothes, Weather game

The aim of these two activities is to encourage children to think about how clothing in particular is affected by weather conditions. They also show how some types of clothing may be suitable for use in more than one type of weather, whilst others are specific to one weather situation. In Weather game on page 7 it may be best to encourage the children to work in pairs. Each pair will need a dice and must understand that they should show it three times, once for the season, once for the weather and once for the activity.
Extension: Tell the children to change the weather conditions and activities then replay the game and draw the resulting pictures.

Pages 8 and 9: Drying out and Investigating the school climate

The aim of these two activities is to suggest some ways in which children can start to investigate microclimate. The term microclimate simply refers to the climate of a very small area, such as around a school. Microclimate can be very important, for example, some classrooms may never see the sun all year and remain cold, whilst others may be hot, even in winter. Or again, some parts of the school site may always be windy or feel very exposed. Other places may always seem to catch the first frost. These activities provide just two ideas for investigating how quickly different surfaces dry out and for observing and recording microclimate at different sites around the school.
Extension: Ask the children to investigate other aspects of the school's microclimate, for example where would be the best place to put a new bench so that it is out of the wind and not in shadow? Where does frost linger? Which are the warmest or windiest classrooms?

Pages 10, 11, 12, 13, 14 and 15: UK Weather forecasts 1 & 2, Patterns to the weather and European weather

The aim of these activities is to help children become accustomed to weather maps, in particular to the different symbols and conventions used on such maps. The other purpose is to help children become familiar with the different parts of the UK and Europe which are often mentioned in forecasts. It is useful at this point to show video tapes of television forecasts and study both what they show and how they show it. Similarly, weather maps from newspapers can play a part in developing children's understanding of what such maps show. The Patterns to the weather activity is also designed to illustrate the range of elements mentioned in a forecast, i.e. temperature (maximum and minimum), precipitation, wind speed, wind direction and cloud cover.

Extension: Ask the children to make up their own forecasts for the UK or Europe on the basis of either records they have kept or forecasts they have seen. Tell them to use their own symbols and write out a full description like the one on page 12.

Pages 16 and 17: Relief rainfall and Convectional rainfall

The aim of these activities is to highlight the processes by which rainfall is generated in relation to relief and convection. The activities summarise the changes in water vapour as a result of cooling and condensation to form firstly clouds and secondly rain. Teachers may find these activities useful summaries of relief and convectional rainfall, or they may wish to use them as an integral part of the initial teaching process. Both can provide a useful precis of each child's understanding of the processes involved and the resultant changes.

Pages 18, 19 and 20: The Beaufort scale of wind speed

The aim of this activity is to help the children envisage the effects of different wind speeds on the environment. Ask the children to think carefully about what they will draw in each picture on the basis of the written description and in particular how each picture will differ from the one before and the one after.

Extension: Use the pictures and the Beaufort scale to estimate wind speed each day for a month and use the pictures to illustrate the changes.

Page 21: Wind directions

The aim of the activity is to highlight the fact that for much of the year Britain's winds blow from the south-west. This is the prevailing wind direction.

Extension: Tell the children to use a blank wind rose to record wind direction at school each day for a month. What is the prevailing wind direction?

Pages 22 and 23: Mountain weather and Rescue

The aim of these activities is to help children to think about the effects of severe weather and of rapid weather changes. In each case the teacher can add to the level of difficulty by removing some of the descriptions or artwork and encouraging the children to suggest their own version of events.

Extension: Ask the children to draw a cartoon strip of a story involving a rapid change in weather such as a thunderstorm at a summer fête, or person afloat on a boat in fog.

Pages 24 and 25: Snowstorm and Winter sports

The aim of these activities is to encourage children to think about the positive and negative effects of snow. Encourage them to talk about their escape from the trapped bus in 'Snowstorm' before they write about it, to ensure they have a logical sequence of events. In the case of 'Winter sports' ask them to describe each clue on the back of the sheet as well as circling them on the picture.

Extension: Ask the children to write stories under the titles 'Too much' and 'Too little' to describe the effects of floods and drought on people in the UK or abroad.

Pages 26 and 27: Hurricane! 1 and 2

The aim of these activities is to illustrate how devastating weather events can be and what precautions people can take to minimise the disastrous effects of such events. Make sure the children understand what a hurricane is, using the description on page 26 before discussing the types of advice given and the reasons behind such advice.

Extension: Ask the children, using an atlas and a blank world map, to draw in the track of hurricanes across the Caribbean as described in newspapers and on television each September and October.

Pages 28, 29, 30 and 31: Climates around the world: Delhi, Amsterdam, In Salah and San Francisco

The aim of these activities is to help children understand the range of data shown on climate graphs of rainfall and temperature. The teacher will need to ensure that the children understand the scales used on the graphs and how to plot the data. Make sure they shade in the first rainfall data lightly so that the second data can be easily distinguished in a different colour. The graphs show the features of four of the world's main climates: Monsoon, West European, Desert and Mediterranean. Teachers may want to elaborate on this with some pupils and use atlases to locate each place then find other parts of the world with the same climate.

Extension: Ask the children to look through their atlases to find climate graphs for the Equatorial climate and the Polar climate.

Page 32: World climates

The aim of this activity is to enable pupils to see how the world can be divided up into different climatic types.

Extension: Using an atlas, ask the children to shade in the West European type of climate, the Continental type of climate and the Monsoon climate.

National Curriculum: Geography

The activities in this book support the following requirements of the PoS for KS2 from the geography National Curriculum:

Geographical Skills
Pupils should be taught to develop and apply the following geographical skills:
- identify and ask questions about geographical features and issues, including through field work and using instruments, such as rain gauges, to make measurements;
- gather, record and analyse evidence, drawing conclusions and communicating their findings;
- use appropriate geographical vocabulary;
- make and use a variety of maps, symbols and keys at a variety of scales;
- use secondary sources, including pictures and photographs;
- use the contents pages and index in an atlas.

Places
People should be taught:
- about the relationships between the features of the localities and the nature and location of human activities;
- about similarities and differences between localities.

Themes
Pupils should be taught:
- how site conditions can influence the weather, *eg temperatures in the shade and in the sun, wind speed in sheltered and exposed sites;*
- about seasonal weather patterns;
- about weather conditions, including extremes, in different parts of the world.

Scottish 5-14 Curriculum: Environmental studies – Social subjects

Attainment outcome	Strand	Attainment targets	Level
Understanding people and place	Knowledge and understanding	Aspects of the physical environment: • ways of measuring and recording weather; • some of the causes of climatic patterns in Britain and the wider world; Ways in which places have affected people: • ways in which weather in differing places affects people and nature and ways in which people adapt to it; • how extremes of weather and climate can disastrously affect people and places.	D D D
	Collecting evidence	Observe events for a particular purpose. Interpret maps. Use thermometer.	C C C
	Recording and presenting	Complete tables, graphs.	C
	Interpreting and evaluating	Identify cause and effect.	C

Northern Ireland Curriculum: Geography

Attainment Target 1: Methods of Geographical Enquiry
Pupils should have opportunities to:
- follow routes marked on maps;
- use the eight points of the compass;
- locate places in atlases using the contents page, the index, and latitude and longitude.

Attainment Target 2: Physical Environments
Pupils should have opportunities to:
- recognise the effect weather has on their daily lives and in other areas of the world;
- recognise seasonal patterns in weather;
- be aware that other parts of the world experience weather different from their own;
- study the idea of climate and how it differs from weather;
- recognise that water can occur in various forms.

Attainment Target 4: Place and Space
Pupils should have opportunities to become familiar with:
- the significance of the lines on maps including latitude, longitude, the Equator, the Tropics.

What is the weather?

Weather is the day-to-day change in sunshine, temperature, rain, cloud and wind at any one place. The weather is what is happening in the area. The pictures below show some of the things which make up weather.

● Number the pictures 1–6 and then describe the weather in each.

● Using these pictures, on the back of this sheet, write down all the ways in which weather affects us. Add any ideas you can think of which are not shown in the pictures.

● Describe what the weather today is like (a) in the morning and (b) in the afternoon. Mention temperature, wind, rain and clouds.

Weather and clothes

● Look at the weather symbols below and label each one from
this list:

Sunshine   Lightning   Rain   Snow   Fog   High wind

● In the box next to each piece of clothing below draw the weather
symbol that best fits the use of the clothes. (There may be more than one.)

   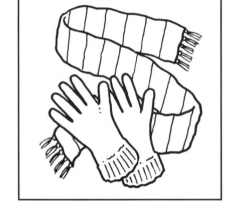

 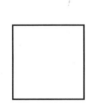   

● Now put the clothes into two sets; (a) those which are useful for
all types of weather; (b) those which are only used in one or two types
of weather.

● Name _____

Weather game

People wear different clothes for different types of weather, and in different seasons.

● You will need a dice. Throw the dice three times and use the table below to find out (1) the season; (2) the weather; and (3) what you are doing. Then write the season, the weather and the conditions at the top of the first box and draw a picture of a person wearing the correct clothes for the conditions.

● Do this again for the second box.

● In the third box write down today's season and weather then choose an activity and draw a picture of yourself in the correct clothes.

Dice number	Season	Dice number	Weather	Dice number	Activity
1	winter	1	heavy rain	1	going to school
2	spring	2	drizzle	2	going shopping
3	summer	3	sunshine	3	in the car
4	autumn	4	breezy	4	at the coast
5	winter	5	cloudy	5	cycling
6	spring	6	storm	6	in the garden

1	2	Today
season _____	season _____	season _____
weather _____	weather _____	weather _____
activity _____	activity _____	activity _____

● Name _____

Drying out

● Use the colour code on drying out times in the matrix below to shade in the corresponding area shown on the map.

● Now carry out a survey of the area around your school and home. Map the different surfaces of grass, water, tarmac, tile and concrete, then in groups, after a rain shower, time how long each one takes to dry out. Station one person next to each surface to carry out the timing. Shade in your map of the area to show how fast places dry out.

Drying out speed   **Colour**

pond   : does not dry out   blue
grass   : dries slowly   green
wildlife area : dries very slowly because of   brown
                marsh and trees
tarmac and   : dries quite quickly   red
paving slabs
tiles   : dry very quickly   yellow
soil   : dries slowly   black

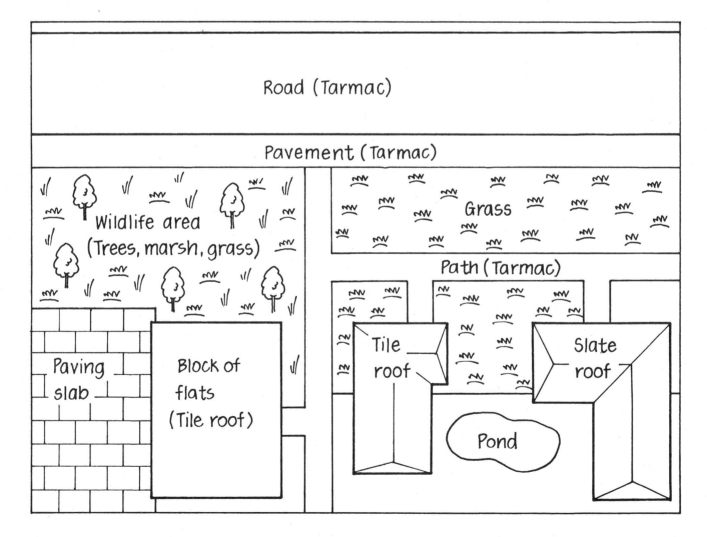

Investigating the school microclimate

● Carry out a survey of conditions in three different places around the outside of the school building but within the school grounds.

● Make a note of the date, time and general weather conditions on the table below.

● Take a thermometer with you to measure the temperature, and leave it for a few minutes in each place to allow it to register the correct temperature. For each site write in the words or figures which best describe conditions at that point. Mark these survey points on a plan of the school.

Date _____

Time _____

General weather conditions _____

Possible descriptions of conditions

	Wind	Cloud	Temp.
A	Still, no wind	totally overcast	cold under 8°C
B	gentle breeze	partly cloudy	warm 8–25°C
C	very strong wind	no cloud	hot over 25°C

Site 1

Wind	Cloud	Temp.

Site 2

Wind	Cloud	Temp.

Site 3

Wind	Cloud	Temp.

● Name _____

UK weather forecast – 1

Here is a weather forecast map for Britain in July. The symbols show
what the weather will be like in different places.

● Answer the following questions:
* Name three areas that will have rain.
* Which areas will have some sunshine?
* Which areas will have thunderstorms?
* Which areas will have hail?

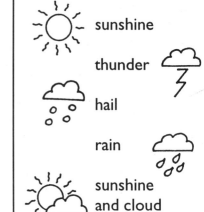

UK weather forecast – 2

Here is a weather forecast map for Britain in January. The
symbols show what the weather will be like in different places.

● Answer the following questions:
• What will the weather be like in London
and the South-East?
• Name three areas which will have snow.
• Name two areas which will have sleet.
• Give the forecast for someone travelling
from Birmingham to Cornwall.
• Give the forecast for a plane flying from
Belfast to Edinburgh and then London.

● Name _____

Patterns to the weather

'Good evening. Tomorrow hilly areas in the West like the Lake District will have heavy rain, with thunder and lightning. Northern Ireland will have sleet or even snow showers. Eastern areas will be cloudy with some sunshine but Norfolk and Suffolk will have sunny clear skies. In the West temperatures will be about 8°C in Cornwall and Devon but only 4°C in Western Scotland and 2°C in Northern Ireland. Inland temperatures will only rise to 3°C over the West Midlands and will stay at 0°C or even −1°C over Kent and Sussex. Winds over the country will be from the south-west and will be moderate to strong, with gales over parts of the Western Isles of Scotland.'

● Read what the weather forecaster is saying about the weather, then use the symbols to plot the weather on the map of Britain opposite.

● Use an atlas to find the places mentioned.

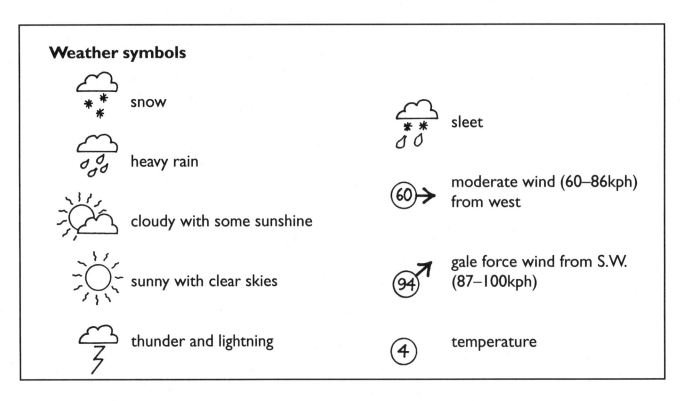

Patterns to the weather (continued)

European weather

The two maps below and opposite show how Europe's weather is expected to change over twenty-four hours.

● Give the forecast changes in both morning and afternoon and include details of wind speed and direction, cloud cover, rain or other precipitation and temperature for the following countries:

- Northern France
- Southern France
- Southern Spain
- Eastern Germany
- Italy
- Norway
- Poland
- Sweden
- Greece

Europe: weather forecast up to 12.00 noon

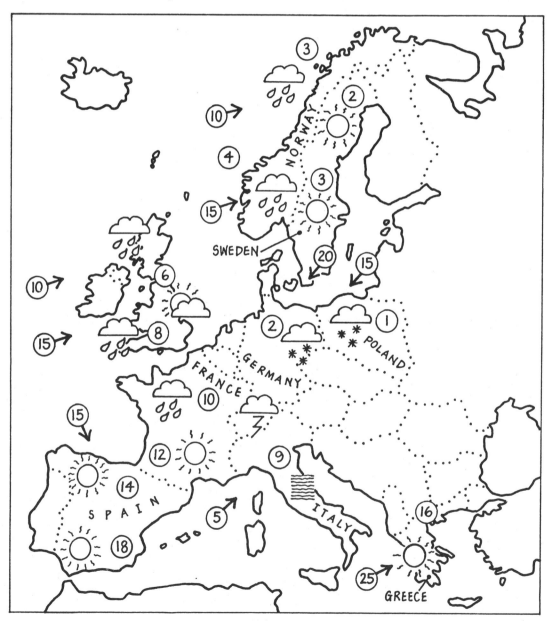

European weather (continued)

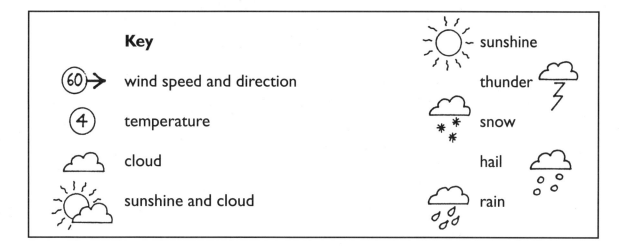

Europe: weather forecast 12.00 noon to 2200 hrs

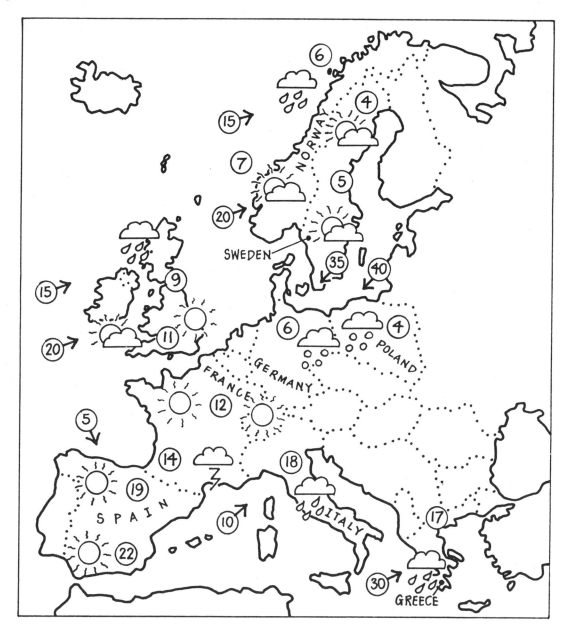

Relief rainfall

● Look at the diagram below.

Air is being forced to rise over mountains. As the air rises the water vapour in it cools. Eventually the water vapour condenses to form tiny droplets of water which hang in the air as clouds. If the clouds are forced to continue rising the water vapour in the air is cooled still further. Then it condenses to form large droplets of water which fall as rain. Once over the hills or mountains the air descends. As it descends the condensation stops and the clouds start to break up.

● Complete the diagram below by adding labels using the text above.
● Use an atlas to find three places in the world where this happens.

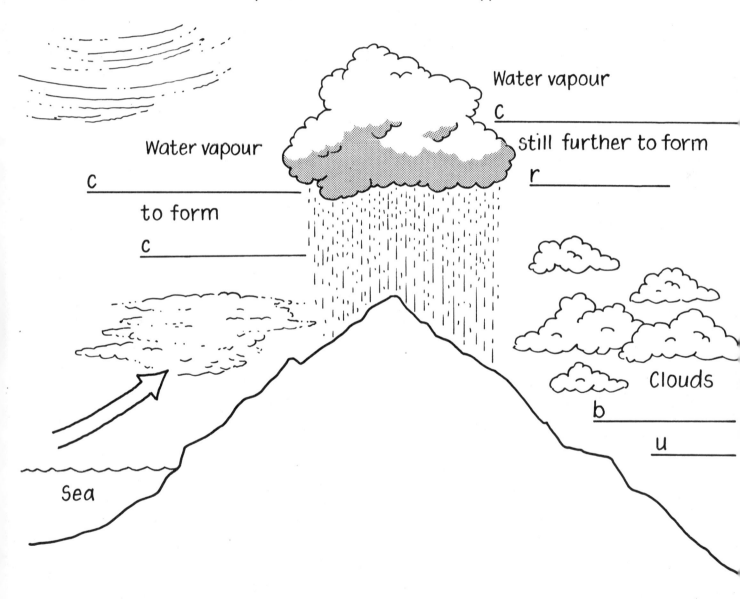

Water vapour

c _____

still further to form

r _____

Water vapour

c _____

to form

c _____

Clouds

b _____

u _____

Sea

Convectional rainfall

● Look at the diagram below which shows the processes which lead to convectional rainfall. Use the diagram to fill in the spaces in the account below then copy it into your exercise book.

When air is h _____ by the sun it starts to _____ .As the air _____

the water vapour in the air is _____ .Tiny _____ are formed which

hang in the _____ as _____ .The air continues to rise and so the _____

_____ is _____ even further. Condensation takes place and large droplets fall

as _____ . Often convectional rainfall comes in h_____ d_____ .When

the sun goes down the air is no longer _____ , so it no longer _____ so the

rain _____ .

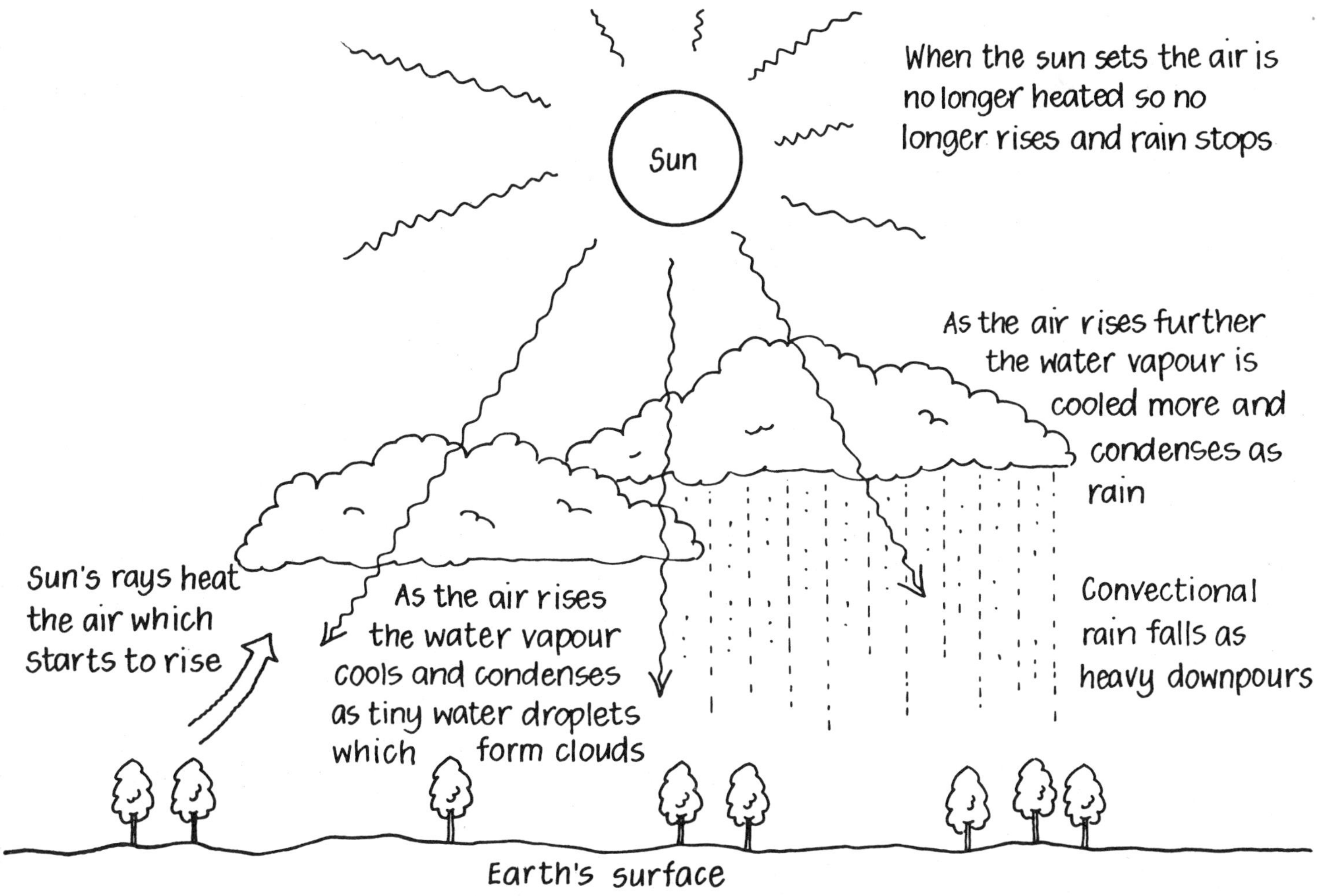

Sun

When the sun sets the air is no longer heated so no longer rises and rain stops

As the air rises further the water vapour is cooled more and condenses as rain

Sun's rays heat the air which starts to rise

As the air rises the water vapour cools and condenses as tiny water droplets which form clouds

Convectional rain falls as heavy downpours

Earth's surface

● Use an atlas to name three areas of the world where convectional rainfall is a regular event.

● Name _____

The Beaufort scale of wind speed

The speed of the wind is measured by the Beaufort scale. This was invented in the nineteenth century by Sir Francis Beaufort as a system for judging wind speed. The Beaufort scale has 13 points (0 to 12). Zero on the scale represents no wind, and 1 is a very slight breeze. Each level has a description so that people can work out how fast the wind in their area is blowing.

● Look at the descriptions of wind speed below then draw pictures in the boxes on the next two pages to illustrate each level on the scale. Two have been done for you.

The Beaufort scale			
Beaufort number	Descriptive title	Effects	Wind speed in kph
0	Calm	Smoke rises vertically.	0–2
1	Light air	Direction shown by smoke but not wind vane.	3–5
2	Light breeze	Wind felt on face; leaves rustle, vane moves in the wind.	6–11
3	Gentle breeze	Leaves and small things in constant motion; wind extends light flag.	12–19
4	Moderate breeze	Raises dust and light paper; small branches are moved.	20–29
5	Fresh breeze	Small trees in leaf begin to sway; crested waves appear on lakes.	30–39
6	Strong breeze	Large branches in motion; whistling heard in telephone lines, umbrellas used only with difficulty.	40–50
7	Moderate gale	Whole trees in motion; people bend forward to walk into the wind.	51–61
8	Fresh gale	Breaks twigs off trees.	62–74
9	Strong gale	Chimney pots and slates blow away as do TV aerials.	75–86
10	Whole gale	Trees uprooted, roofs blow away.	87–101
11	Storm	Some houses lose roofs and walls. More trees are uprooted, trees fall on houses and cars. Power lines down.	102–121
12	Hurricane	Houses flattened, caravans destroyed, trees flattened.	over 122

● Name _____

The Beaufort scale – 2

0

1

2

3

4

5

The Beaufort scale – 3

6

7

8

9

10

11 and 12

Wind directions

The wind rose is used to record wind direction over a week or a month. The list of directions at the bottom of the page shows which directions the wind blew from in one month in Birmingham.

● Use the wind rose to record these directions. First put the 8 compass points on the wind rose. Then, for each day fill in one box along the arm of the rose corresponding to the wind direction. The first one has been done for you.

● What is the *prevailing wind direction* (i.e. from which direction does the wind blow most often)?

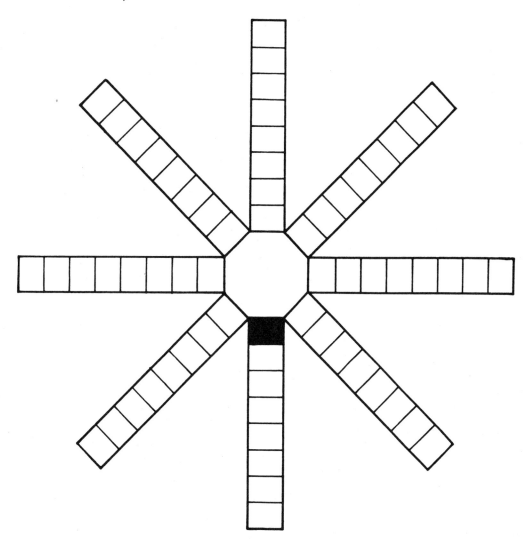

S, SW, SW, S, E, NE, SE, N, NE, S, SW, SW, W, SW, SE, N, N, E, SE, SW, W, NW, SW, S, SW, W, NW, W.

Mountain weather

Weather in the mountains can change very quickly. These changes can cause problems for people as the story below shows.

● Complete the story by drawing the pictures and giving it an ending.

1	2
1 Three climbers set out in sunshine towards a mountain.	2 As they climb on to snow the clouds build up.
3	4
3 Snow starts to fall and the climbers have to shelter in their tent.	4 The wind rises, the blizzard continues and the tent is blown away.
5	6
5 The weather starts to clear but the climbers are lost.	6

Rescue!

The weather around Britain's coasts can change a lot during the course of a single day. The story below shows how these changes can create dangers. Then the rescue services have to be called out.

● Complete the story by writing the missing text, drawing the pictures and giving it an ending.

1	2
1 Five yachts set out on a race on a sunny, breezy day.	2
3	4
3 Suddenly the sail of one yacht tears as the cloud builds up and the wind strengthens.	4 The yacht tips over in the high seas and heavy rain as the wind grows even stronger.
5	6
5	6

Snowstorm

● Imagine you are one of the passengers on the bus which has
crashed in a snowstorm. You are stranded on an isolated country road.
On the back of this sheet write a story about the event, describing
(a) where you were going; (b) how the crash happened; (c) how you
felt; (d) how you and the other passengers coped in the cold blizzard;
and (e) how you were rescued.

● Name _____

Winter sports

The picture below shows a village in the Alps in the summer.

● Put a ring round each clue that you can find to show that this place gets a lot of snow in winter.

SNOWTIME HOTEL

ICE RINK

HOTEL SKI

SKI-RUN

PRACTICE SHED

ACME SNOW

DRY-RUN

DRY-RUN

Hurricane! (I)

The weather in a hurricane

Before the hurricane arrives clouds build up and the wind becomes stronger. Gusts of wind come with rain showers. As the wind gets stronger the rain gets heavier and becomes torrential. Wind speeds can reach over 160kph and over 100mm of rain can fall in just one hour! Thunder and lightning become continuous. Suddenly the centre of the hurricane, called the 'eye' passes over. For 2–3 hours the skies are clear, the wind drops and the sun comes out. But then the winds start again, stronger than ever, together with the torrential rain and thunder. Eventually the hurricane moves away and people start to pick up the pieces.

● Read the advice to people in the USA about what to do when a hurricane is expected.
● Read the description of the weather changes in one hurricane.

KEEP YOUR RADIO OR TV ON... AND LISTEN TO LATEST WEATHER BUREAU ADVICE TO SAVE YOUR *LIFE* AND POSSESSIONS

BEFORE THE WIND AND FLOOD	HAVE GAS TANK FILLED.... CHECK BATTERY AND TIRES.	HAVE SUPPLY OF DRINKING WATER. STOCK UP ON FOODS THAT NEED NO COOKING OR REFRIGERATION.
HAVE ON HAND FLASH-LIGHT, FIRST AID KIT, FIRE EXTINGUISHER, BATTERY-POWERED RADIO.	STORE ALL LOOSE OBJECTS: TOYS, TOOLS, TRASH CANS, AWNINGS, ETC. BOARD OR TAPE UP ALL WINDOWS.	GET AWAY FROM LOW AREAS THAT MAY BE SWEPT BY STORM TIDES OR FLOODS.

DURING THE STORM	STAY INDOORS... DON'T BE FOOLED IF THE CALM "EYE" PASSES DIRECTLY OVER ... AND DON'T BE CAUGHT IN THE OPEN WHEN THE HURRICANE WINDS RESUME FROM THE OPPOSITE DIRECTION.	LISTEN TO YOUR RADIO OR TV FOR INFORMATION FROM THE WEATHER BUREAU, CIVIL DEFENSE, RED CROSS, AND OTHER AUTHORITIES.

AFTER THE STORM HAS PASSED	DO NOT DRIVE UNLESS NECESSARY. WATCH OUT FOR UNDERMINED PAVEMENT AND BROKEN POWER LINES.	REPORT DOWNED POWER WIRES, BROKEN WATER OR SEWER PIPES TO PROPER AUTHORITIES OR NEAREST POLICEMAN.
	USE EXTREME CAUTION TO PREVENT OUTBREAK OF FIRE, OR INJURIES FROM FALLING OBJECTS.	USE PHONE FOR EMERGENCIES ONLY. JAMMED SWITCHBOARDS PREVENT EMER-GENCY FROM CALLS GOING THROUGH.

YOUR ABILITY TO MEET EMERGENCIES WILL INSPIRE AND HELP OTHERS

U.S. DEPARTMENT OF COMMERCE • WEATHER BUREAU

Hurricane! (2)

● List all the precautions people in the USA are advised to take when a hurricane is expected.

_____

_____

_____

_____

_____

_____

● Why are people advised to beware the 'eye ' of the hurricane?

_____

_____

_____

● Why are people advised to take care immediately after a hurricane has passed?

_____

_____

_____

● What damage might people find when they do return home? Describe the scene in the first box and draw a picture of it in the second box.

1	2

Climates around the world

Delhi and Amsterdam – rainfall

Different parts of the world have very different weather. The word **weather** describes the daily changes in sunshine, cloud, wind and rainfall at any one place. The average weather of a place over the course of one year is called its **climate**.

● Complete the graph below which shows how much rain falls in Delhi in each month during the year by using the figures beneath the graph.
● How much rain in total falls in Delhi in a year?
● Now plot the figures for Amsterdam in a different colour using the second set of figures below.

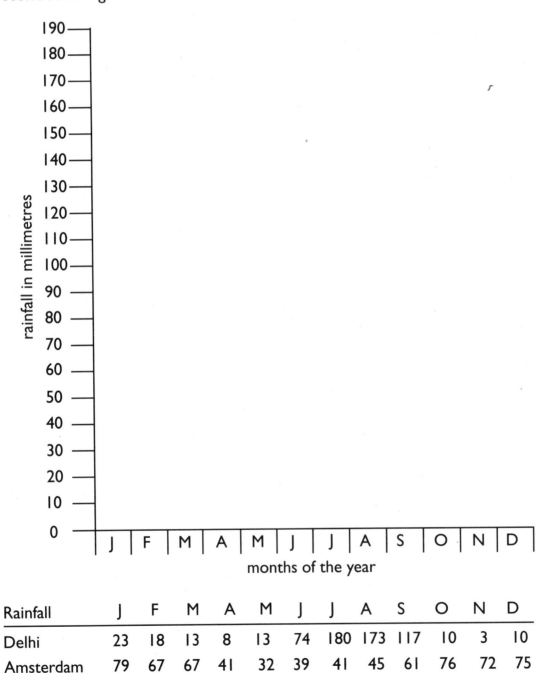

months of the year

Rainfall	J	F	M	A	M	J	J	A	S	O	N	D
Delhi	23	18	13	8	13	74	180	173	117	10	3	10
Amsterdam	79	67	67	41	32	39	41	45	61	76	72	75

Climates around the world

Delhi and Amsterdam – temperature
● Complete the graph which shows how the temperature changes each month in Delhi, using the figures below. Plot each month with a dot and then join up the dots. The first three months have been done for you.
● Now plot the figures for Amsterdam from the second set of figures.

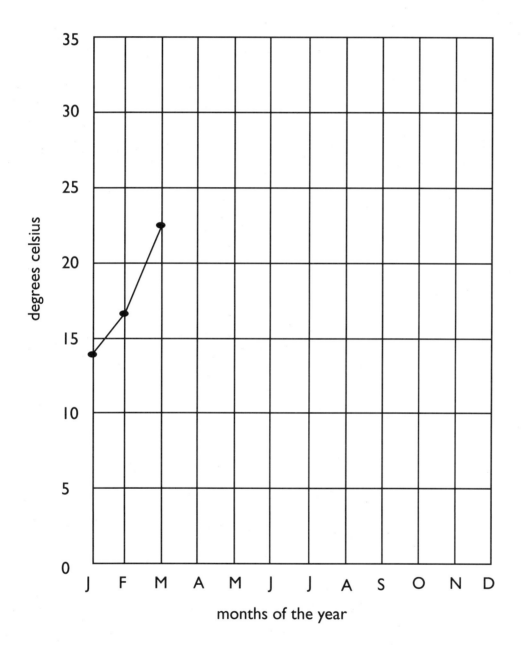

months of the year

Temperature in degrees celsius	J	F	M	A	M	J	J	A	S	O	N	D
Delhi	13.9	16.7	22.5	28.1	33.4	33.6	31.4	30	29	26.1	20	15
Amsterdam	1.1	1.9	3.9	7.8	11.7	15.5	17.2	16.7	13.9	9.5	4.7	2.2

● Name _____

Climates around the world

In Salah and San Francisco – rainfall
● Complete the graph to show rainfall each month at In Salah (Sahara) and San Francisco (California), using the figures below. Use a different colour for each town.
● How much rain in total falls in In Salah and San Francisco in a year?

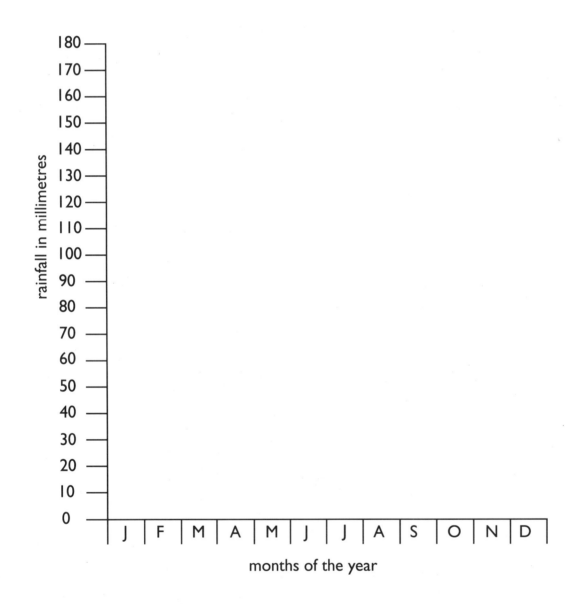

months of the year

Rainfall	J	F	M	A	M	J	J	A	S	O	N	D
In Salah	5	5	0	0	0	0	0	0	0	0	5	5
San Francisco	119	97	79	38	18	3	3	3	8	25	64	112

Climates around the world

In Salah and San Francisco – temperature
● Complete the graph by plotting the temperature each month for In Salah using the figures below. Mark a dot for each month then join them all up.
● Now draw the graph for San Francisco using a different colour.

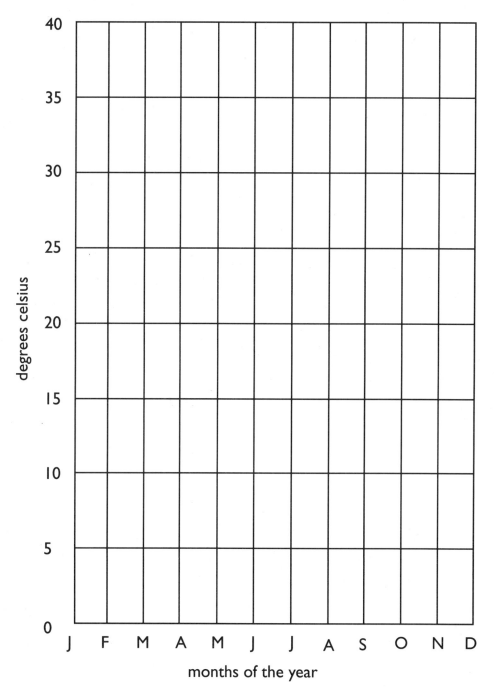

months of the year

Temperature in degrees celsius	J	F	M	A	M	J	J	A	S	O	N	D
In Salah	13.3	16.1	20	25	28.9	29.5	36.7	35.9	32.8	26.7	19.2	14.4
San Francisco	10	11.7	12.5	13.1	13.9	15	15	16.7	16.1	13.9	11.2	6.7

World climates

- Use the key on the world map to shade in four different types of climate shown.
- Use an atlas and draw the Tropic of Cancer, the Tropic Capricorn, the Arctic Circle and the Antarctic Circle to your map.

- Name each line.
- Name five countries which have a Mediterranean climate.
- Name ten cities in places with an Equatorial climate.

Name _____

KEY			colour
○	Equatorial		green
▨	Desert		yellow
+	Polar		blue
△	Mediterranean		red

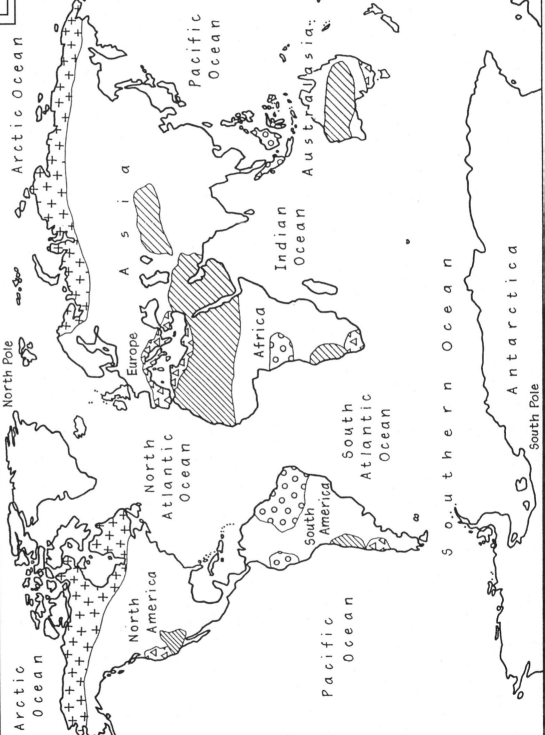

Arctic Ocean

North Pole

North Atlantic Ocean

North America

Pacific Ocean

Arctic Ocean

South America

South Atlantic Ocean

Europe

Asia

Africa

Indian Ocean

Australasia

Pacific Ocean

Southern Ocean

Antarctica

South Pole